The Great Songs of Elton John

Wise Publications
London/New York/Sydney

Exclusive Distributors:
Music Sales Limited
8/9 Frith Street, London W1V 5TZ, England.
Music Sales Pty. Limited
120 Rothschild Avenue, Rosebery, NSW 2018, Australia.

This book © Copyright 1988 by Wise Publications
UK ISBN 0.7119.1478.8
Order No. AM71127

Designed by Pearce Marchbank & Phil Levene.
Cover photography by L.F.I.
Compiled by Peter Evans.

Music Sales' complete catalogue lists thousands of
titles and is free from you local music shop,
or direct from Music Sales Limited.
Please send a cheque/postal order for £1.50 for
postage to Music Sales Limited, Newmarket Road,
Bury St Edmunds, Suffolk IP33 3YB.

Printed in England by
JB Offset Printers (Marks Tey) Limited
Marks Tey

The Great Songs of Elton John.

Your Song

Words & Music by Elton John and Bernie Taupin

Slow, but with a beat

6

Country Comfort

Words & Music by Elton John & Bernie Taupin

3. Down at the well they've got a new machine,
   Foreman says it cuts manpower by fifteen,
   But that ain't natural, so old Clay would say,
   He's a horse-drawn man until his dying day.

   (Repeat Chorus)

4. Now the old fat goose is flying 'cross the sticks,
   The hedge-hog's done in clay between the bricks,
   And the rocking chair's a-creaking on the porch,
   Across the valley moves the herdsman with his torch.

   (Repeat Chorus)

Rocket Man

Words & Music by Elton John & Bernie Taupin

Moderately slow, with a beat

Goodbye Yellow Brick Road

Words & Music by Elton John & Bernie Taupin

Moderately slow, in 2

Candle In The Wind

Words & Music by Elton John & Bernie Taupin

21

Crocodile Rock

Words & Music by Elton John & Bernie Taupin

Sorry Seems To Be The Hardest Word

Words & Music by Elton John & Bernie Taupin

Slow lament

What have I got to do to make you love____ me ____

What have I got to do____ to make you care.____ What do I do when light-ning strikes_

____ me ____ And I wake___ to find_____ that you're not there

It's sad___ it's so sad_ Why can't_ we talk_ it o - ver___ Al - ways seems to me____ that
(it's so sad)

sor - ry seems to be___ the hard - est word

word. What do I do to make you love_

Song For Guy

By Elton John

Life is - n't ev - er - y - thing,

is - n't ev - er - y - thing,

is - n't ev - er - y -

Verse 3
Once I never could hope to win
You starting down the road
Leaving me again, The threats
you made were meant to cut me down
And if our love was just a circus
You'd be a clown by now.

Nikita

Music by Elton John
Words by Bernie Taupin

Hey, Nik - it - a, is it cold ___ in your lit - tle corn - er
Do you ev - er dream of me? ___ Do you ev - er see the let - ters

of the world? You could roll a - round the globe, ___
that I write? When you look up through the wire,

nev - er___ know._

Sad Songs (Say So Much)

Music by Elton John
Words by Bernie Taupin

Moderately, with a blues feel

mf

Guess there are times when we all need to share — a lit - tle pain, — oh, it it - tle to write — down, it down — and iron - ing out the when ev - 'ry sin - gle

If some - one else is suf - fer - in' e - nough, — need — all

F   Bb/F F

C°

(So) Turn 'em on,_____ turn 'em on,_____ turn on those

sad songs._ When all hope is gone_____ why don't you

tune in and turn_ them on?_____ They reach in - to your

room, oh,_____ just feel_ their_ gen - tle touch._

12658 10/91